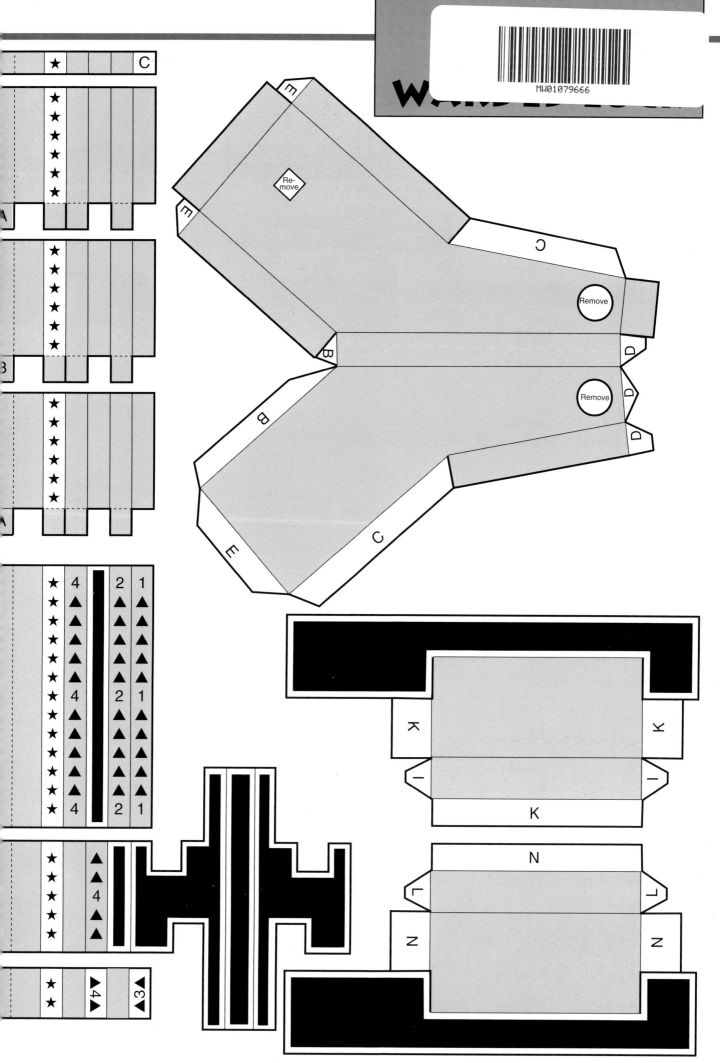

The 13 pieces for the Warded Lock are on this page and pages 3 & 5.   1

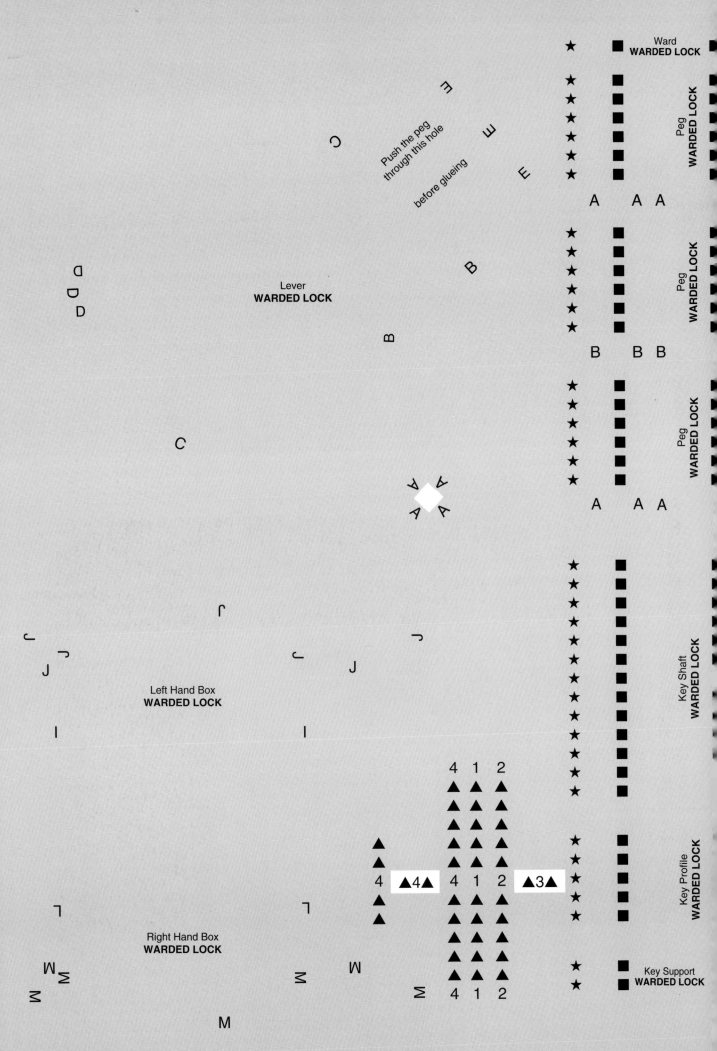

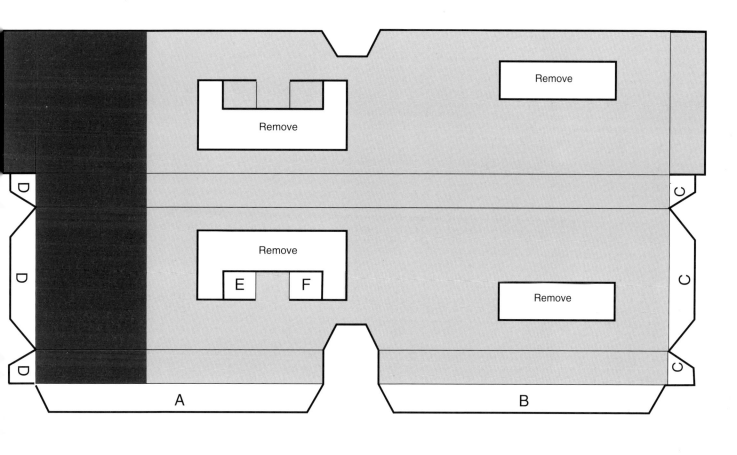

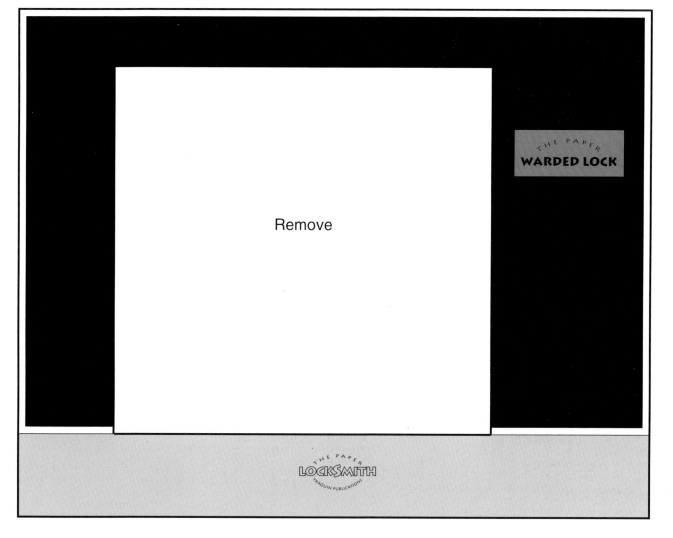

The 13 pieces for the Warded Lock are on this page and pages 1 & 5.

C

B

A

D

O

F

E

D

C

D

Lever
WARDED LOCK

P

P

P

P

P

P
Frame
WARDED LOCK

O

O

4

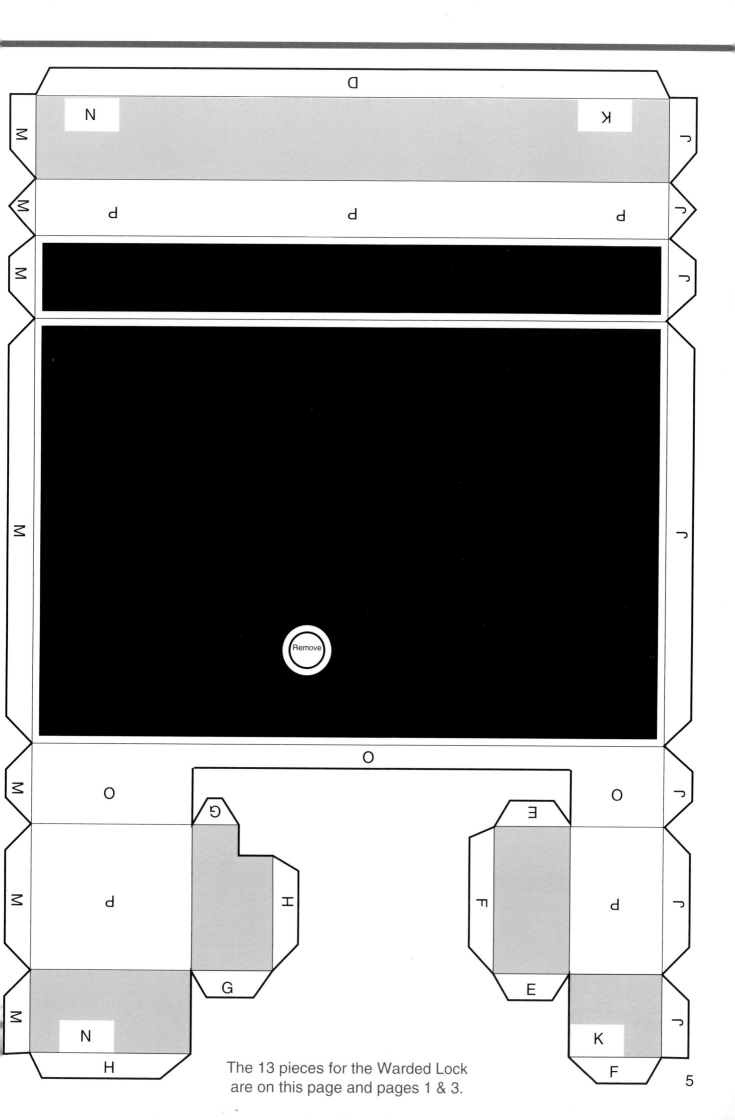

The 13 pieces for the Warded Lock
are on this page and pages 1 & 3.

Base
WARDED LOCK

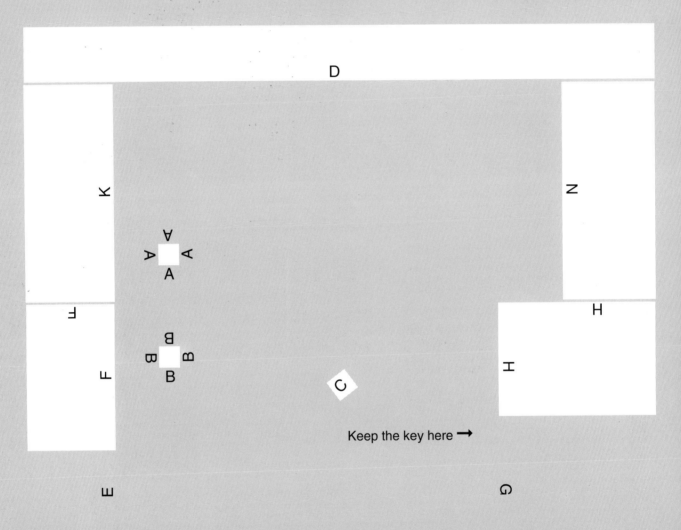

Keep the key here →

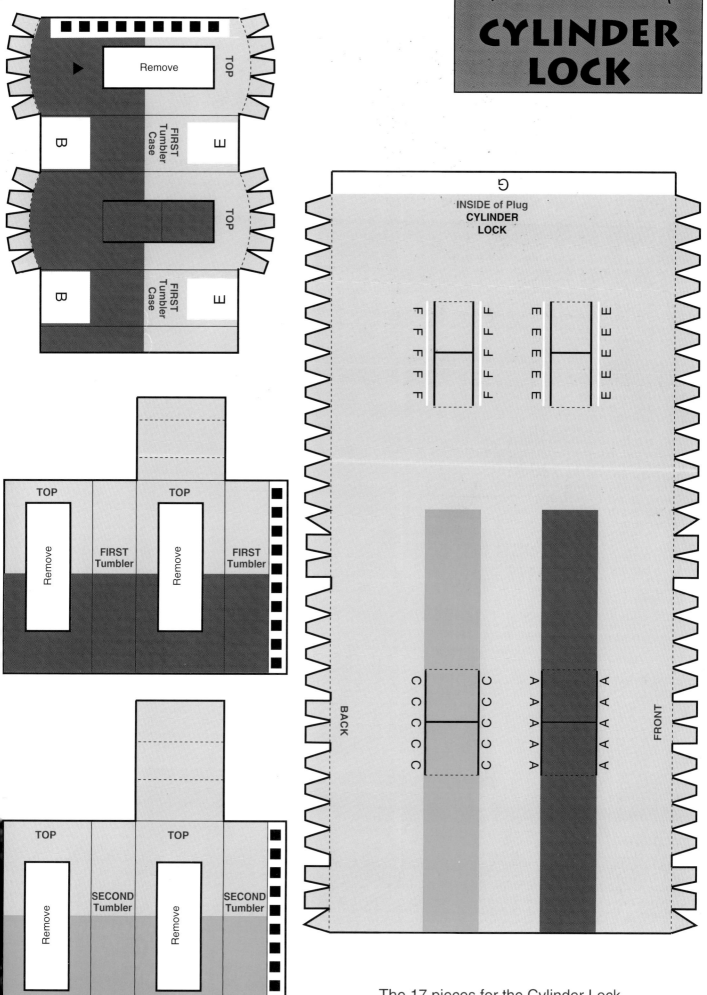

The 17 pieces for the Cylinder Lock
are on this page and pages 9, 21 & 23.

First Tumbler Case
CYLINDER
LOCK

First Tumbler
CYLINDER
LOCK

Second Tumbler
CYLINDER
LOCK

E

B

F

D

G

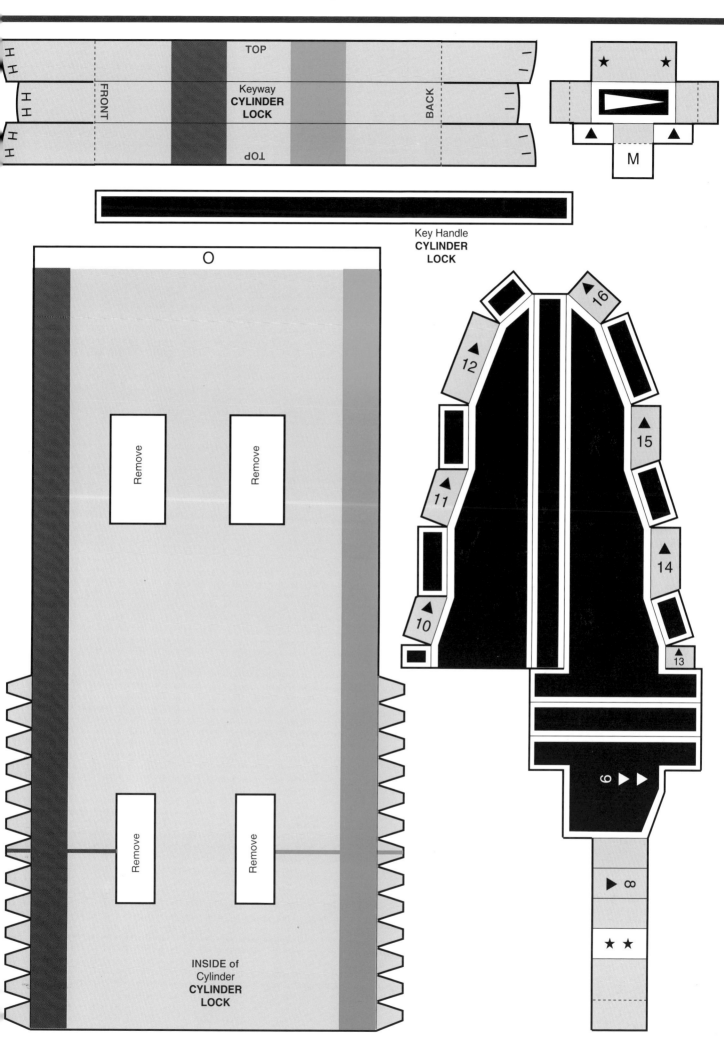

TOP

FRONT

Keyway
CYLINDER LOCK

BACK

TOP

★ ★

▲ ▲

M

Key Handle
CYLINDER LOCK

O

Remove

Remove

Remove

Remove

INSIDE of
Cylinder
CYLINDER LOCK

12

16

11

15

10

14

13

9 ▶ ▶

8 ▶

★ ★

The 17 pieces for the Cylinder Lock are on this page and pages 9, 21 & 23.

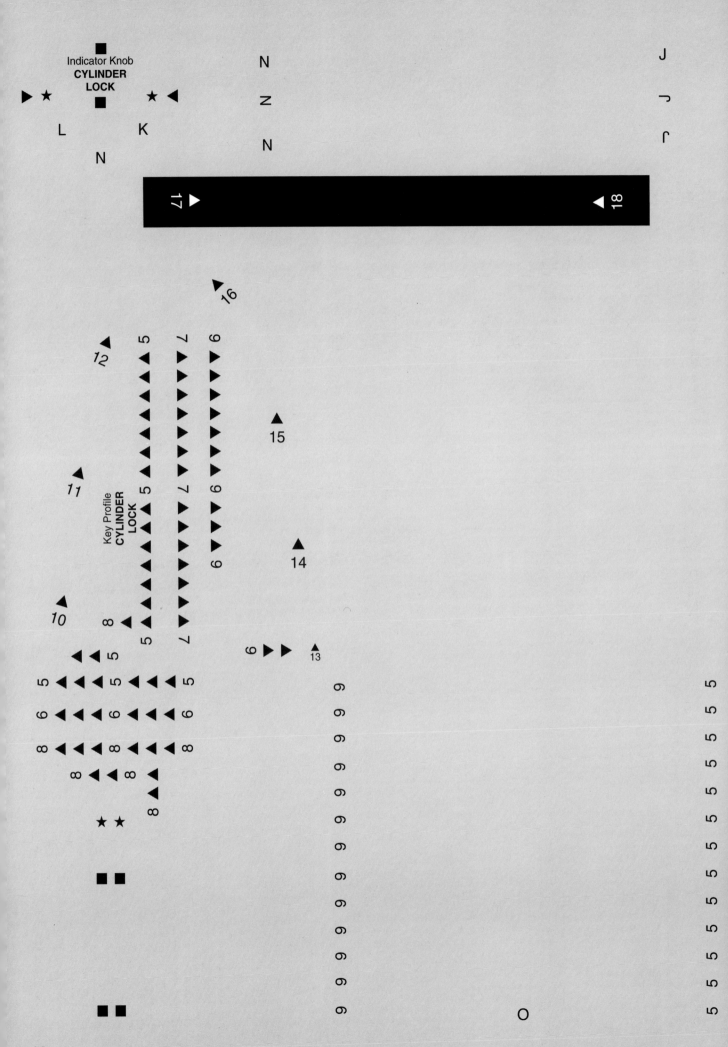

THE STORY OF LOCK MAKING

ROB IVES

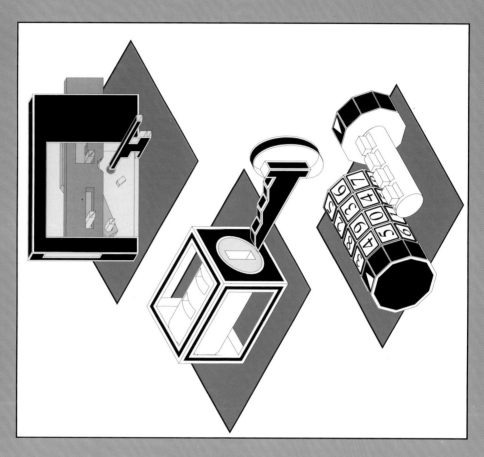

Tarquin

1 899618 03 1

WHAT MAKES A SUCCESSFUL LOCK DESIGN?

The story of locks is a fascinating one. It combines the delight in the design of clever mechanical gadgets with the satisfaction of solving a real and important problem.

People like to feel secure, both in terms of their personal safety and in that of their possessions. Personal security is simpler in principle, as it is always possible to barricade oneself inside a building or a bedroom. For this purpose, a lock is not necessary. Any kind of bolt or bar fixed to the inside of a door can prevent someone entering quietly and without applying considerable force. Windows can be barred or shuttered. They can also be made very small or so that they will never open. However all these solutions to the problems of personal safety, while effective, require that the person remains inside. There is also always the disadvantage with this kind of security that if that person is taken ill or suffers some other serious misfortune while inside, then no-one else can enter the room without breaking in.

The problem of keeping valuables safe is a different one. No-one would wish to spend their life in a barred and bolted room looking after their valuables! If you hire guards to do it for you, then there is always the problem, well expressed in the Latin phrase, "Quis custodet custodies?" or "Who guards the guards?" It is clear that a mechanical security system has many advantages and the history of locks is really the story of finding suitable methods.

A successful lock is one which is able to allow easy access to those who are authorised and which denies it to everyone else. The commonest way of opening a lock is through the possession of a key of some kind. It can be mechanical, made of metal or plastic, or the key could be the knowledge of an entry code or a sequence of operations. Those who have the key can open the door easily. Those who do not are prevented from doing so. Since it is true that no system can be absolutely secure, the question of time delay is also important. The longer it takes to make an unauthorised entry, the more likely a thief is to be discovered and the rightful owners to return. A very simple lock may be sufficient to deter an inexperienced opportunistic thief, whereas an elaborate security system is needed to keep (say) a gang of bank robbers at bay. There is a balance to strike.

An interesting piece of lateral thinking occurred in the past. A family wished to keep a large hoard of silver coins safe in a country where there were no banks or secure vaults to put them in. Their solution was to mix them with a very large amount of sand and then to fill a large pit in the garden with the mixture. The argument was that a thief would take a long time to dig out and sieve through the sand to find the coins, whereas the rightful owners could spend as long as they wished. It is amusing to think of the advantages and disadvantages of this idea!

This book does not concern itself with sandpits or vaults, but it is able to demonstrate the principles of locks very well. By their very nature, the internal structure and the way that a lock works has to be hidden from view and although we often use them it is not generally known how they work. Studying plans and diagrams may help, but these three-dimensional working models are able to do so in a much clearer and more dynamic way.

Make these three models and read this minibook. It is a truly fascinating subject!

FINGERPRINT LOCKS

Each of us has a unique set of fingerprints and if a computer could be trained to recognise a fingerprint, then the advantages in using it as the key to an electronic lock are considerable. There is no key to lose, no combination to forget and short of some rather macabre surgery, no way in which anyone else could gain access.

Fingerprint Patterns

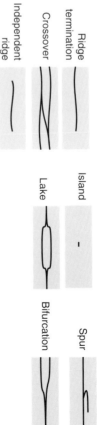

Ridge termination	Island
Crossover	Lake
Independent ridge	Spur
	Bifurcation

Since fingerprints are already widely used to identify criminals and millions are stored in police records, there is a considerable incentive to find a cheap and easy way of digitalising them and storing them in a computer. Searching for the owner of a print found at the scene of a crime would then become much easier, faster and more reliable. Neural networks are being developed which work by looking for key features and then digitalising them. These key features and their relationship to each other should even be able to determine which finger the print is from. Any of the technology needed for a successful fingerprint lock will surely be developed from this kind of research.

Another approach which is being tried is a lock which you have to look into. As he or she does so, the lock scans the pattern of blood vessels at the back of the eye. It is thought and hoped that these patterns are as individual as fingerprints. If the pattern matches, then the door would open.

Signature recognition systems are already here and are used for cash-less banking. Not only is the computer able to recognise the pattern of the signature, but also the pressure applied and the order in which the strokes are made. Such systems already make forgery more difficult and could also be used as the basis for an electronic lock which opens when you sign it.

Ultimately, it is likely that the computer will make all of these systems unnecessary. Just as it is not necessary to check the fingerprints or retina prints of your friends before letting them into your house, when sophisticated face recognition systems become cheap and easy to make there will be no more need for keys. Your house lock will recognise you and let you in. When you have visitors you will train it to let them in also.

One can also imagine the ultimate lock; a trainable cat-flap. Your cat would be recognised and let in, but not all the other cats in the neighbourhood! A truly world-shattering invention!

Rob Ives

If you have enjoyed this book then there may be other Tarquin titles which will interest you. They are available from Bookshops, Toy Shops, Art/Craft Shops, or in case of difficulty directly from Tarquin Publications, Stradbroke, Diss, Norfolk, IP21 5JP, England. For an up-to-date catalogue of Tarquin books, please write to the publishers at the address above.

LOCK-PICKING

You may feel that there is an unhealthy interest in lock-picking in this book. Yet it is the challenge of the potential thief which has driven the development of locks. If there were no thieves, then there would be no need for locks at all, a simple catch to prevent the wind blowing open the door would be all that is needed. A manufacturer who does not consider and attempt to thwart the future attentions of a lock-picker cannot hope to design a successful lock. Even without dishonest intentions there is a considerable intellectual pleasure in seeing how to pick locks. However, if you do decide to practice on real locks, make sure that they are your own!

THE EARLIEST LOCK

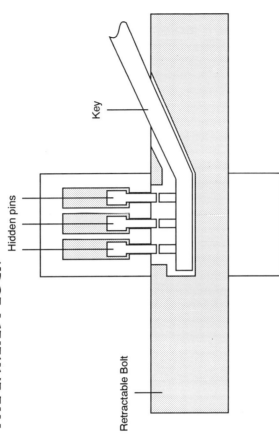

More than four thousand years ago the ancient Egyptians invented what was probably the first lock, certainly it is the oldest which still exists. The key was shaped rather like a tooth brush and when it was inserted into the lock, the 'bristles' lifted hidden pins and allowed the bolt to be retracted.

Even this very early example of a lock illustrates the clear separation of the functioning of a lock into three parts. The first part is the bolt which holds the door closed and prevents entry. The second is the lock mechanism which allows the bolt to be withdrawn only by someone with possession of the correct key. The third part is the key. Look out for these three functions in any lock which you examine.

The Greeks and Romans also developed locks and it was the Romans who invented the kind of lock which we call the 'warded' lock and which is the first model to make. A ward is a protrusion of metal and it is there to ward off attempts to open a lock with the wrong key. Then, as now, it was important not to lose a key and the Romans sometimes wore their keys on their fingers as rings.

LOOKING TO THE FUTURE

Writing about the future of lock design can only be speculation but it is interesting to try. It is almost certain that electronics will play a bigger and bigger part. Every year computers become cheaper, smaller and more powerful and this looks set to continue. Computers are able to perform an enormous number of calculations in a fraction of a second and even the simplest modern microprocessor has sufficient power to handle a formidable combination lock or swipe card system. However, where computers are not so strong at present is in the area of pattern recognition. If this weakness could be overcome, then many ingenious, convenient and secure new lock designs will become possible.

PATTERN RECOGNITION

The human brain is a remarkable tool for recognising patterns. We are able to recognise thousands of different faces, even people we have not seen for years. We are still able to recognise people when they have changed their clothes or hair colour. With a little familiarity we can even distinguish between identical twins. We are able to recognise handwriting, hair styles, voices, even the way people walk. Until recently, computers had found this type of pattern recognition impossible. The traditional approach to programming a computer where every single step of the program is spelt out in minute detail is simply not practicable. It is virtually impossible to describe in computer language to describe the computer each individual step and stage which is required to recognise a simple object, let alone a human face. A new approach has had to be found and researchers are now investigating the possibility of imitating some of the structures of the brain. In particular, what are called neural networks. It is hoped that computers set up in this way will be able to learn to program themselves, rather as a human brain is able to do when faced with a new problem. Already there has been some success and programs are being developed which can learn to recognise simple patterns.

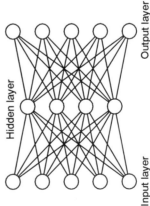

In these devices there are generally three layers of neurons. The first is connected to the outside world, for example, via a television camera and is where the information enters the system. The centre layer is for computation and the third layer is concerned with the output. This is the layer that passes on the results of the calculation to the next stage. In the case of a lock it would pass on an instruction to a solenoid to draw back the bolt.

Each of the neurons on each layer is connected to all the neurons in the next layer. By varying the strengths of these connections the network can be made to learn. This neural network technology is already used in speech recognition systems and can be trained to recognise individual voices and accents. In a similar way it can be trained to recognise handwriting and both the success rate and the speed of operation are steadily improving.

THE WARDED LOCK

The warded lock is the simplest of all the locks that are currently in use. It works by having a ridge or ward of metal attached to the body of the lock. This prevents the key from turning unless the key has a cut-out in the corresponding place.

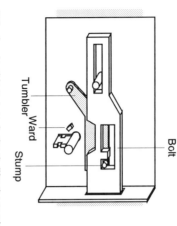

Tumbler Ward Stump Bolt

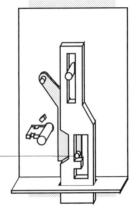

The stump prevents the bolt from moving

Ward Cut-outs to match ward Key

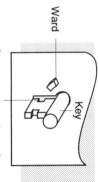

If the key is able to turn, it simply lifts the tumbler with the stump clear of the bolt and then slides the bolt into position. Make the model and see exactly how it works. Because of the simplicity of design, warded locks are cheap to produce but not very secure. Some models may have as few as ten different keys. However, even without access to a key, this type of lock is surprisingly easy to pick. With just a simple understanding of the internal workings of the lock, it is not difficult to see how to find out the positions of the wards and how to make a key to match a given lock. Choose a suitable blank key and cover its face with a thin layer of wax. Put the key into the lock and turn it gently. Where the blank face of the key touches a ward an impression will be made in the wax. File this section of the key away and it will then pass the ward and hopefully open the lock.

To prevent such a simple approach, some locks have several wards in staggered positions. The new key will not pass the next ward until the whole procedure has been repeated. Although increasing the number of wards slows down the process of making a key impression, it does not prevent it.

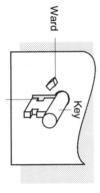

Ward Key

Skeleton keys can also be used effectively against warded locks. They avoid the time and trouble it takes to file away the cut-outs. They work by having the absolute minimum of metal in the key and are therefore able to bypass most wards without encountering them at all. A professional locksmith will have a collection of different skeleton keys and with them can gain access to a wide variety of locks where the keys are missing or lost. It is clear why they are named as they are.

MASTER KEYS FOR DISC TUMBLER LOCKS

The disc tumbler lock is sometimes used in a simple master key system although, like the warded lock, it is difficult to implement a full 'Key-Master-Grand Master' system.

Ordinary key engages right hand side of gate

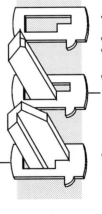

Master key engages left hand side of gate

A relatively secure master key system can be implemented with very little modification to the original lock design. The diagram shows that it can be achieved by the careful use of shaped cut-outs in the tumbler. Each disc tumbler has a gate cut on the left hand side to one height and on the right to another. By having shaped keys which engage either the left or the right gates it is possible for there to be two different keys which will open the left hand side of all gates in the group lock. Thus if a group of locks are manufactured so that the left hand side of all gates in the group are identical then a single master key will open them all.

MASTER KEYS FOR PIN TUMBLER LOCKS

By far the most secure system for implementing a master key system is one using the pin tumbler lock and this is the one commonly used nowadays in hotels. Systems can be created with master keys, grand master keys, even great grand master keys, all without detracting seriously from the security of the lock. On page 10 it was explained how in this design of lock each pin is divided into two parts and hence has a shear line to allow the key to turn. Master systems rely on having each pin divided into three or more parts and hence having two or more possible shear lines.

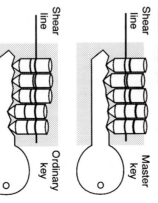

Shear line Master key

Shear line Ordinary key

MASTER KEYS FOR LEVER LOCKS

Two bellies

Master keyhole Ordinary keyhole

This kind of system is only rarely seen, but it has been produced. It works by having two separate keyholes, one for the normal key and one for the master key. The lever has two bellies (also called saddles) of different heights and a key in either keyhole will be able to move the stump of the bolt through its gate, thus moving the locking bolt in or out.

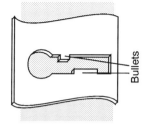

OTHER KINDS OF WARD

Wards are also used in the keyhole itself to prevent an incorrect key from being inserted. This type of obstruction is called a case ward or a bullet. It is not unique to a traditional warded lock, but is used on many other types of lock as well. Bullets can give a considerable measure of extra security. In simple situations like the one illustrated here, they could be bypassed by judicious use of a file but nowadays they are mostly built into the body of the lock. Look at car keys in particular to see the pattern of grooves on them. They explain why the keys from one car will almost never fit into the lock of another car, let alone turn and start the engine.

PSYCHOLOGY AND MYSTERY

Even an immensely complex warding system can be bypassed with experience and bent wire. In the Middle Ages the tendency was to use psychology, secrecy and cunning tricks in order to mislead, dissuade or injure the burglar.

Locks were made to look impressive and impregnable, and sometimes the real keyhole was hidden behind secret doors. False keyholes were prominently placed in order to mislead a prospective burglar into spending time picking locks which would not open the door anyway. Another approach was to make important treasure chests with five, ten or even twenty locks so that it would take any thief a very long time to pick them all. This of course was not very convenient for the rightful owner, who also had to open all of them each time he wanted something from the chest. As a result, others were made with a huge number of bolts, but all retracted by a single key. This type looked extremely secure to the purchaser, but they were in fact rather easy to open, especially as it must be realised that the lock which controlled them all was the same old type of warded lock, well known to the lock pickers of the era.

More active and drastic measures were sometimes employed and traps were set for the unwary. One chest was designed so that when the lid was opened it revealed an ornate inner lid complete with obvious finger holes. If anyone attempted to remove this lid by putting their fingers into these holes, a powerful spring would cause steel jaws to snap together and trap or even amputate them. Other locks were designed which fired steel darts or guns if a hidden safety catch was not operated first and there is at least one documented case of a locksmith being seriously injured whilst demonstrating his lock to a prospective client.

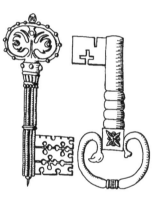

In order to show off their talents and skills locksmiths made what were called 'Masterpiece' locks.

Craftsmanship, artistry and ingenious cunning were used to overcome the weakness of the basic lock mechanism. Keys were ornate and often carved in the shape of animals or complex patterns, and lock plates were engraved with the crest of the owner.

MASTER KEY SYSTEMS

Large buildings such as hotels or offices often need a system which allows some people to enter any room but yet to have individual keys for each door. For example, in a hotel each guest needs a key which will open their own door but no others, and cleaners need to be able to enter many rooms. While they could be given a duplicate key for each room and thus carry round a large bundle, it is more convenient and much cheaper if there is a single key which will open all the doors. Such a key is called a master key.

In large hotels there may be a need to allow one cleaner access to one floor and another access to another floor. Yet the manager will want a single key which will give access to all rooms. The diagram above shows a typical hotel key system. Obviously in a real hotel there would be more keys at each layer of the pyramid, but the principle is clear. For instance, the management would have a 'Grand Master' key, the cleaners for each of the three floors a 'Master' key and each of the guests on each floor would have an 'Individual' key. The design of master keys of course depends very much on the type of lock in use. As with locks in general, the warded lock is the easiest to implement but also the least secure.

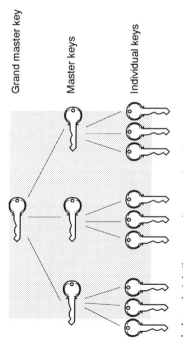

Grand master key

Master keys

Individual keys

MASTER KEYS FOR WARDED LOCKS

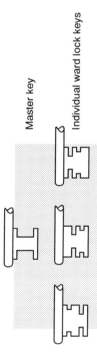

Master key

Individual ward lock keys

As we have already seen, it is not generally possible to create very many different shapes of key for a warded lock. With only 10 or 12 possible shapes it is not possible to introduce grand master keys into the system so the pyramid can only have two layers. The diagram above shows a typical ward key and master key setup. The individual keys will only open one lock but the master key, by having its sides cut away, is able to open all of them. It is easy to see why this system is not very secure. How simple it would be to take a standard key and with some deft work with a file, convert it into a master key. Notice how closely the master key compares with the skeleton key mentioned in the section on ward locks. In fact skeleton keys were the first master keys.

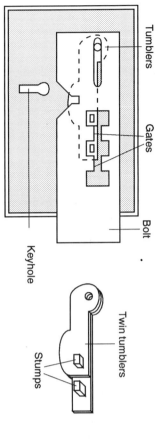

Tumblers · Gates · Bolt · Keyhole · Twin tumblers · Stumps

In 1778 Robert Barron patented the first lock to move away from the principle of the warded lock. Although he still used wards for extra security, the lock did break new ground. It had two tumblers and when the correct key was turned, both were raised. Only if both tumblers were raised to the correct height could the stump catch on the gate in the bolt and prevent movement. If either was too high or too low, its stump would catch on the gate on the bolt, a reversal of the situation in a modern lever lock. The stump was on the tumbler and the gate on the bolt, a reversal of the situation in a modern lever lock. In 1790, Moses Bird patented a four lever lock which did not use wards at all. It can be said that this design was the direct forerunner of the modern lever lock.

THE LEVER LOCK

A typical key from a five-lever lock

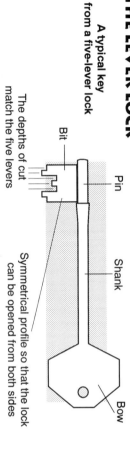

The depths of cut match the five levers

Bit · Pin · Shank · Bow

Symmetrical profile so that the lock can be opened from both sides

The lever lock is commonly used nowadays in house doors and is often a mortice lock, so called because it is recessed into a door. The action is similar to that of the warded lock model as the key is used to raise a lever and slide the bolt in a single movement. However, there are differences. Firstly there are several levers, typically three or five, and secondly, each has to be lifted to an exact height for the bolt to move and the key to continue to turn.

DEADLOCKS

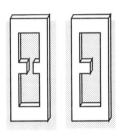

As in the warded lock, the turning movement of the key lifts the levers to allow the stump of both to pass through their gates. In later designs the width of the gate was restricted so that each lever had to be raised to a precise height, greatly increasing the security. In both types, once the bolt has been extended, it cannot be pressed in again without the key. Locks with this characteristic are called deadlocks. You can test this property on the model.

A QUESTION OF SECURITY

The model lock with four rings and ten positions for each has 10x10x10x10 or ten thousand possible combinations. If you could try one combination every second, it would still take nearly three hours to work through them all. For a safe lock like the one opposite with three wheels and one hundred numbers on the dial, there are 100x100x100 or one million possible different combinations. Even if it were possible to try one combination every second (and it would not be) it would take over eleven and a half days, working night and day to work through them all!

With cheaper locks it is sometimes possible to pull gently on the lock as you turn the rings and to feel where the gates are and there are locks with false gates to thwart this possibility. The safe lock is a lot more difficult to pick but this is where the most expensive mechanical combination locks have reached the point where they are virtually unpickable in any reasonable length of time.

ELECTRONIC COMBINATION LOCKS

Electronic locks have no moving parts and so there can be no give-away clicks as tumblers or pins move into position. There are no slight movements which could reveal the position of a hidden gate. However it would be a brave enthusiast who would claim that an electronic combination lock is absolutely unpickable. It certainly cannot be picked in the traditional way, but one should never lose sight of the fact that the lock itself must know what its combination is or it would not open when that number was typed in. The information must be stored somewhere and a determined hacker may be able to access it. There are sufficient examples already of how youthful hackers have found their way into 'secure' and top secret computer systems to leave room for doubt that any system is absolutely unpickable.

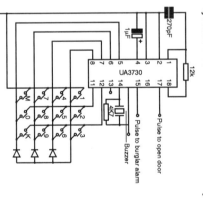

Combination locks are normally constructed using a standard integrated circuit. This is then connected to a motor or solenoid which retracts the locking bolt and allows the door to be opened. This circuit diagram shows the eighteen pin integrated circuit UA3730 which can be set up to respond to a combination lock number of up to twelve digits.

To open the lock the number has to be typed in followed by a single press of the M-key. If three wrong numbers are entered, a pulse is sent to a burglar alarm. This circuit can easily be re-programmed to respond to any chosen number and this is achieved by connecting pin 13 to earth, typing in the new number and then pressing once on the M key.

Electronic combination locks do offer a serious barrier to a typical potential burglar and, in practice, they are impossible to pick. With no clues or feedback to help, realistically, the only way to open the door is to know the code or to use brute force. A typical door lock with a four figure code has ten thousand possible combinations and to discourage anyone from working systematically through them, is usually programmed to stop responding and sounds an alarm if three wrong numbers are entered. It returns to normal after a pre-set time delay. If it did not return to normal automatically, any attempt to break in would prevent the rightful owner from opening the lock later.

THE FIVE-LEVER DEADLOCK

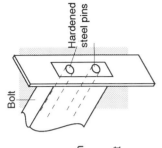

Bolt

Hardened steel pins

This kind of modern high quality lock offers a high degree of security and insurance companies often insist that they are fitted to the doors of houses. Such locks are very difficult to pick anyway, but extra measures are also taken to foil the prospective intruder. To prevent anyone from cutting through the relatively soft brass of the bolt, hardened steel pins are buried within it. Their ends can be seen by looking at the exposed end of the bolt. Also, to strengthen the door against being forced open, a steel box is usually inserted within the frame.

In the model, the force of gravity causes the lever to drop after it has passed through the gate, and it must be held upright for it to work. In a real lock this force is provided by a spring, otherwise safebreakers would be able to open safes just by turning them on their sides or upside-down!

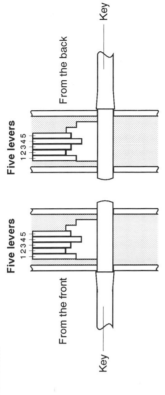

From the front

Key

Five levers
1 2 3 4 5

From the back

Key

Five levers
1 2 3 4 5

The constraints of paper engineering require that the key to the model works from one side of the lock only. However, it is important that a real door lock can be operated from both sides. So that this can happen, the key bit must be symmetrical and in a five-lever lock the third and fifth levers have to be identical. This restriction has the additional advantage that the lock body can be narrower and it will therefore fit fully inside the timber of the door. Not only does this improve the elegance of the fixture, but it increases the resistance to physical attack on the whole mechanism.

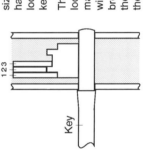

Three levers
1 2 3

Key

Two and three-lever locks usually have a similar design and size of key as a five lever version. Although they appear to have the same number of teeth, some are used to open the lock from the front and some from the back. Once again the key blade must be symmetrical.

The importance of removing the key from a locked lever deadlock and hiding it, is now apparent. An intruder who has managed to break into a building, perhaps through a skylight, will be unable to leave by the door with the booty without breaking down the door or picking the lock. One is noisy and the other takes a long time. Both actions considerably increase the chance of being caught!

7

COMBINATION LOCKS

The major advantage of combination locks is that there are no keys to lose or to be stolen. They can be mechanical or electronic. With some designs, the combination is fixed when it is manufactured. With others, it can be altered easily, indeed whenever the door is open.

The model combination lock to cut out and make will be recognised to be similar to the type often used for securing bicycles. You can set the combination to whatever you wish as you glue the model together, but as it cannot be changed later, it is a good idea to write it down and to keep it in a safe place. Otherwise you will have to work through 10,000 possible combinations!

Each rotating ring has ten positions and each conceals a hidden gate. When the correct combination is entered, the four gates line up and the centre core can then be pulled out. To lock it, the central core is pushed home and the four rings are randomly rotated. In a real bicycle lock, the ends of a strong chain would be attached to each of the two parts.

A combination lock on a briefcase works in a similar way, although the internal layout is a little different. The principle is the same and the briefcase catch can only be opened when the hidden gates of the three or four wheels line up.

LOCKS FOR SAFES

Combination locks in safes work in a rather different way. A pack of (usually) three wheels is linked to a single dial on the front of the safe. Each wheel has a gating on it and only when all three line up can the bolt be withdrawn and the door opened.

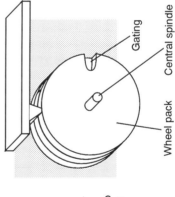

Gating

Central spindle

Wheel pack

The wheels have protrusions on them so that by rotating the same central spindle alternately clockwise and anticlockwise, the individual wheels are engaged and turned in sequence. For instance, to open a lock with combination 14-54-78, first rotate the dial anti-clockwise two whole turns and then on to the number 14. Now rotate the dial clockwise one whole turn and then on to the number 54. Then turn anti-clockwise again to the number 78 and the lock can be opened.

To lock the safe again the door is closed and the dial randomly spun clockwise and anti-clockwise. This disengages the wheels and makes (virtually) certain that the gatings no longer line up. A tug on the door makes certain that they have not been done so by a million to one chance.

14

THE BRAMAH LOCK

In 1784 Joseph Bramah patented his lock. It was a new and interesting design which worked by having a number of slotted sliders running within a slotted disk. The slotted key pushed the sliders downwards against the pressure of a spring and only when all the slots in the sliders were lined up with all the slots in the disc could the key turn the barrel and the lock be opened.

The diagram shows a version with six sliders although only four of them can be seen in the cross-section. Some versions of the lock had as many as twelve or eighteen. Although difficult to manufacture and expensive to buy, this design was considered absolutely unpickable.

Key

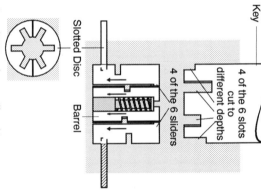
Key
Slotted Disc
Barrel
4 of the 6 slots cut to different depths
4 of the 6 sliders

One was displayed in Bramah's shop window and a prize of 200 guineas offered to anyone who could pick it. In those days this was a very large sum of money indeed and a considerable incentive. However, it remained unclaimed for more than fifty years. This actual lock is now in the Science Museum in London.

A NEW NATIONAL SPORT

Interest in new lock designs grew and in the period of seventy years leading up to the Great Exhibition of 1851, over eighty patents were granted and lock-picking became almost a national sport. The lock mechanism evolved rapidly as lock-pickers employed by some locksmiths attacked the locks made by others and the press was filled with claim and counter-claim. This period is known as the time of 'The Great Lock Controversy'. It was conducted with great publicity and ill-will on all sides.

In 1817 Portsmouth dockyard was robbed and the Crown offered a prize to anyone who could design a lock which could not be picked and which could not be opened with a skeleton key. A year later, Jeremiah Chubb won the prize and he went on to become one of the great lock-makers of all time. However, there were always those on the look-out to find weaknesses in any design and each success by a lock-picker had to be immediately met by a modification to overcome the threat. The state had a great interest in secure locks and so, when an ex-lock-smith convict claimed that he could pick the new Chubb lever lock, he was offered both a free pardon from the Portsmouth prison ship where he was held and a prize of £100, if he could succeed. But after trying for three months, he had to admit defeat and was returned to the ship to complete his sentence. This was greatly to the delight of Mr Chubb and the naval authorities.

However, they were less pleased when Bramah, well-known for having invented his own unpickable lock, criticised Chubb's new design. He claimed that it would be prone to wear and therefore unsuitable for long term use. Chubb proved that this was a false accusation by arranging a public demonstration where a small engine was attached to one of his locks. After nearly half a million operations, the lock still worked perfectly.

INCREASING THE LEVEL OF SECURITY

If the number of pins is increased then the lock becomes harder to pick and some locks with 20 or more have been made. However, this is an expensive solution because they become very complicated to manufacture. A better approach is for there to be fewer pins but for them to be shaped in three-dimensions. A lock can be designed so that each pin has both to be lifted to the correct height and also rotated into the correct orientation. There are a number of different designs using this technique, but one of the most elegant is illustrated here.

This design makes a lock virtually unpickable.

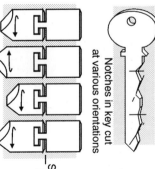
Notches in key cut at various orientations
Shear line

BRUTE FORCE

However, no matter how unpickable and elegant the design, a lock can still succumb to brute force if it is not adequately protected. For instance, an accurately drilled hole may destroy some pins and allow others to drop out. Then the plug can be turned and the door unlocked.

Hardened steel pins are used to protect vulnerable spots even on relatively ordinary locks and for very high security safes and bank vaults, they can be designed so that even if explosives destroy the lock itself, the bolts which hold the door closed will embed themselves still deeper and become yet more difficult to withdraw.

THE CREDIT CARD TRICK

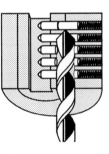
Credit card
Door frame
Door
Lock body
Retracting tongue

This trick is often seen on films and TV. It works supposedly on 'Yale type' locks with a spring loaded bolt. Apparently all one has to do is to push a credit card between the door and the frame and push home the retracting tongue from the lock body. Since this type of lock is not a deadlock, it sounds possible and operating the slider is generally inconvenient in real life, except for last thing at night. What can be done? Simply make the door frame overlap the door by a small amount! It then becomes impossible to insert a credit card and at the same time keeps out draughts. This type of overlap is so common that it is virtually impossible to find an outside door without it. It would seem that credit cards are only able to open doors in films! However, those of a criminal disposition may well be able to acquire a strip of plastic or metal which is flexible enough to bend around the door but strong enough to push back the bolt. If such a material does become readily available, then in future the five lever deadlock may have to replace the Yale on front doors.

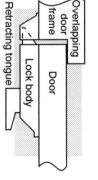
Overlapping door frame
Door
Lock body
Retracting tongue

NEW INVENTIONS

Chubb was an innovator and he added a metal curtain which covered the keyhole as the key turned, making it very difficult to insert lock-picking tools. Another development was the 'detector' lock. It had a special lever which clicked into the locked position if any of the ordinary levers were raised above the gate level. This is exactly what would happen if a lock pick was used or an attempt made with a wrong key. The owner would therefore know that his lock had been tampered with. The detector lever could be reset by turning the correct key backwards, but was very difficult for a thief to reset, once he had set it off.

A. C. HOBBS

Hobbs was the representative of an American lock-maker, Day & Newell, and on arriving in England, he set out to make an impression on the British lock-making world. He certainly succeeded. In London he walked into Chubb's shop and casually picked one of the six-lever locks on display. Chubb was aghast and claimed that it had been a fluke. However, Hobbs seized his opportunity and arranged a public demonstration. In full view, he picked the lock in less than thirty minutes and then relocked it in a further seven minutes. Chubb was forced to make several modifications before he could once again claim to have an unpickable lock.

Hobbs then moved on to tackle the Braman lock. The 200 guinea prize had remained unclaimed for the past fifty years. After ten days of preparation, working four hours a day, Hobbs set up a demonstration and in a few minutes he succeeded in picking the lock in front of Braman himself and a group of officials. As can be imagined, Braman was overcome and upset and he insisted that Hobbs must have cheated in some way. Hobbs then asked for the proper key to be used to demonstrate that he had not damaged the lock. The impartial witnesses decreed that Braman should pay over the money and eventually after a lot of correspondence and delay, he did.

Hobbs used this publicity to promote the Day & Newell 'Parautoptic' lock. The name came from the Greek words meaning 'concealed from view'. The principle was that the levers which operated the bolt should not be the ones moved directly by the key. Turning the key operated some levers which in turn operated others which operated others. In its final version it had twelve levers and a prize of 2000 dollars was offered to anyone who could pick it. This prize was never claimed.

It must be realised that these locks, although of the highest quality, were hand made and very expensive. They were beyond the pockets of all but banks, jewellers and the wealthy. Ordinary people had to rely on the unsatisfactory and insecure ward lock, until Linus Yale (Senior and Junior) entered the field with their mass produced cylinder locks.

TIME DELAY LOCKS

A lock patented in 1831 by William Rutherford of Jedburgh in Scotland is the first example of a time delay lock. It had a circular stop plate operated by clockwork and prevented even the proper key being used until a certain number of hours had passed. This was in response to a spate of robberies where the criminals had seized the key holders, and under threat had made them divulge the combination number or hand over the safe keys. This threat was removed when no-one, including the owner or key holder, could open the lock say, until 8.00 a.m.
This concept is widely used today in banks and you will often see a notice to that effect on the counter. You will also see it on high security vehicles which carry large amounts of cash to and from banks and other businesses. Delay for potential criminals is a serious deterrent.

9

PICKING A CYLINDER LOCK

To pick this type of lock successfully, each individual pin must be pushed up so that its shear line matches that of the cylinders. Although this is a delicate and difficult operation, it is made possible by the slight inaccuracies that inevitably occur in the drilling of the pin chambers.

Exaggerated view of top of lock plug showing drilling inaccuracies

When a small amount of rotational tension is applied to the plug by inserting an L-shaped lever into the key way, one of the pins will be slightly ahead of the others and therefore will be slightly stiffer to move. This is the one which must be raised first by pushing with the lock pick.

When that pin is raised to the shear line, there will be a slight click, which may be heard or felt through the tension tool and it will then cease to be the stiffest one. This process is then repeated on the new stiffest pin until all they have all been lifted. The lock will then open. This sounds an easy process, but of course the differences are minute and any release of the tension in the tensioning tool means that all the pins which have already been picked would drop back in and the lock-picker would have to start again.

Lock pick

Successfully picked tumbler

Tensioning tool applies gentle pressure to plug

COMBATTING THE LOCK-PICKER

Improving the accuracy of manufacture helps to thwart the lock-picker. If the line of pin holes is drilled exactly parallel to the axis of rotation, then no pin would be ahead of another and it would be impossible to know when it had been raised by the correct amount. This method of picking could therefore not be used. Although desirable, this improvement is difficult to achieve in practice and other approaches are needed as well.

Cross section of a standard pin tumbler lock

With the lower part of the pin serrated

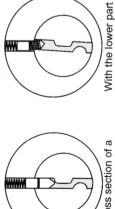

With the upper part of the pin dumb-bell shaped

A locksmith who knows that someone is listening for clicks can design the lock to give false ones. He can do this by carefully shaping the pins. A pin with its lower half serrated like the one in the centre diagram will catch on the shear line, give a click and ease the tension. All without first having been raised to the shear line. Another approach which has been tried is to shape the top part of the pin like a dumb-bell. It will snag just below the shear line and so prevent the lock from opening. It is very difficult for a lock-picker to ease the pressure in this situation without letting other pins drop back.

12

CYLINDER LOCKS

Linus Yale was an inventor of milling machinery and in 1844 he came up with a simple compact design which is still in use today. The principle is not so different from the Egyptian lock introduced on page 3, but instead of a sliding bolt, the lock has a rotating cylindrical core. There are two basic types, one based on pin tumblers and the other on disc tumblers. The disc tumbler lock is the easier and cheaper to produce but it is also less secure.

THE DISC TUMBLER CYLINDER LOCK

The cylinder lock model in this book is of the disc tumbler type. It has two disc tumblers and they are operated by the force of gravity. It is therefore essential to keep the lock the right way up. When the key is inserted into the lock the tumblers are lifted and become completely confined within the plug (the rotating cylinder). This allows it to turn, showing open and closed signs in their usual colours of red and green. Without the correct key one or both tumblers will protrude from the plug and snag on the cylinder, so preventing the plug from turning. In a real lock there would usually be five tumblers and they would be operated by small coil springs.

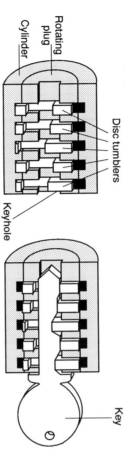

Rotating plug

Cylinder

Disc tumblers

Keyhole

Key

The diagram shows a cross section of a disc tumbler lock. In the first picture there is no key in the lock and each of the tumblers is pushed to the bottom of the cylinder by its spring. In the second the correct key has been inserted and all the tumblers are lined up within the plug. It is then free to rotate. The plug is joined to a bolt and the act of rotation slides the bolt in or out. In contrast to the model, the tumblers in a real lock can be also raised too far and snag on the lock casing on the other side. This feature was included in the early trial versions of the model, but it introduced more complications to the paper engineering than could be justified. The principle however, is clear.

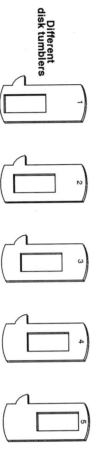

Different disk tumblers

1 2 3 4 5

Within each disc tumbler, the slots can in theory be placed at any height, but they are usually limited to five possible positions. A typical lock of this type has five tumblers and five positions for each, so there are a possible 3125 (5x5x5x5x5) different locks which could be made. In practice, many combinations are not used: for instance, those with four or five identical tumblers. This means that there is a maximum of about 500 different types and different keys. Disc tumbler locks are often used in cars, desk locks and filing cabinets. For higher security situations the pin tumbler version of the cylinder lock is preferred.

THE PIN TUMBLER CYLINDER LOCK

Instead of the single pressed steel disc, this kind of cylinder lock uses metal pins each divided into two parts of varying length. The upper part in contact with the spring is called the roller. Although a basically simple idea, this lock gives a high degree of security. It has the disadvantage that because of the greater accuracy needed to manufacture it, the price is higher.

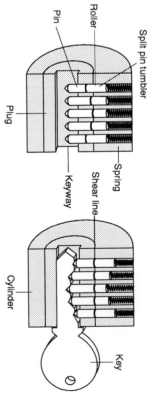

Split pin tumbler

Roller

Pin

Spring

Shear line

Plug

Keyway

Cylinder

Key

When there is no key in the keyway the springs force the two parts of each pin down into the plug and it is therefore unable to turn. When a key is inserted into the lock, it pushes against the pins and lifts them all upwards by differing amounts. The lock and its key are so designed that when the correct key is in place, the shear lines separating the two parts of each split pin all coincide exactly with the shear line between the plug and the cylinder. Once all of the pins are raised in this way, it is possible to turn the key and so unlock the lock. The rotating plug is connected to a separate mechanism which slides the bolt in and out. This is the same as in the disc tumbler cylinder lock.

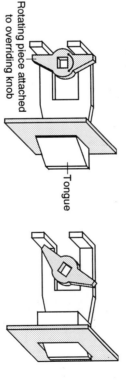

Rotating piece attached to overriding knob

Tongue

Most people will recognise this type of lock as the 'Yale' type and there will almost certainly be one on the front door of your house or flat. It is clear that it is a one-sided lock and the key is not needed to open it from the inside. Usually there is a knob to twist which overrides the lock and slides back the bolt independently. The diagram shows how this is achieved.

This type of lock is not a deadlock and the design does not allow it to be. The bolt which holds the door closed is spring loaded and its protruding tongue is sloped or curved so that the door can be closed without the key. Because the tongue can be pushed back without using the key, such locks usually have a thumb slide for additional security. When it is placed in the locked position, the tongue will not push back and the key will not turn it at all.

Since it is such a common and well-known design, it is an excellent one to use as an illustration of lock picking techniques and the countermeasures which the locksmith incorporates to improve security.

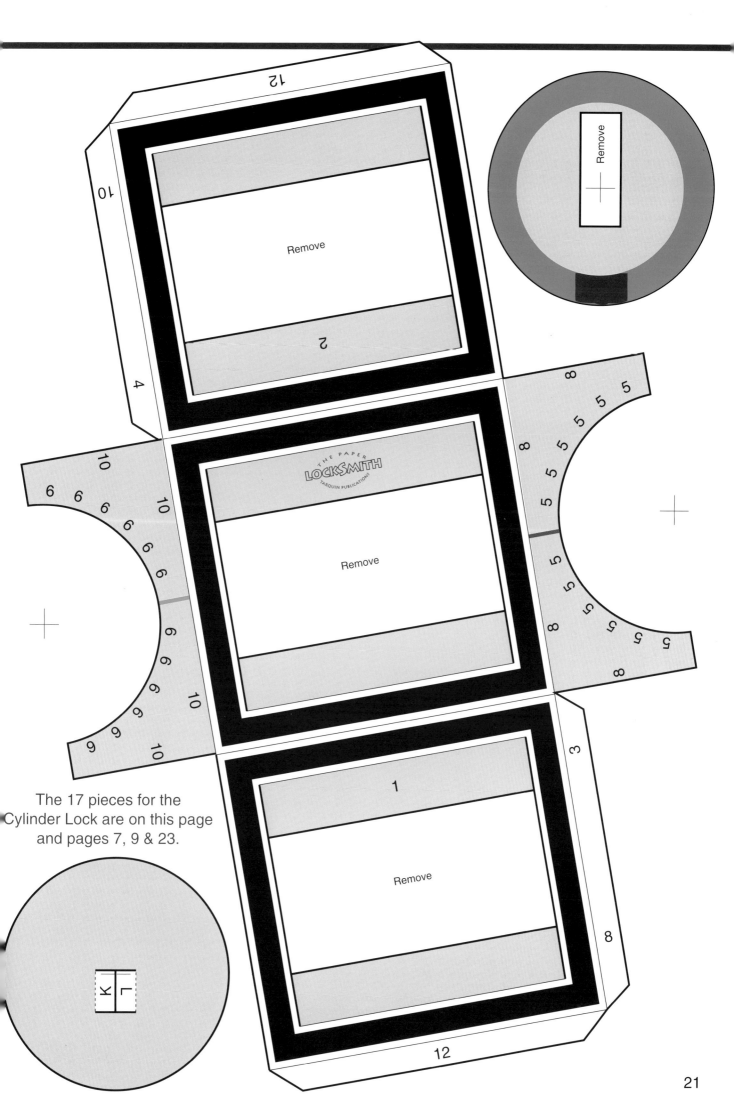

The 17 pieces for the
Cylinder Lock are on this page
and pages 7, 9 & 23.

Remove

Remove

Remove

Remove

THE PAPER
LOCKSMITH
TARQUIN PUBLICATIONS

12
10
4
2
8
5
5
5
5
5
5
5
5
5
5
8
8
8
6
6
6
6
6
6
6
6
6
6
6
10
10
10
10
3
1
8
12
K
L

TOP

J   J

J

Plug Front
**CYLINDER
LOCK**

13

2

4

3

1

Frame
**CYLINDER
LOCK**

14

N N N N N N N N
TOP

Plug Back
**CYLINDER
LOCK**

6

N   N

M

The 17 pieces for the Cylinder Lock
are on this page and pages 7, 9 & 21.

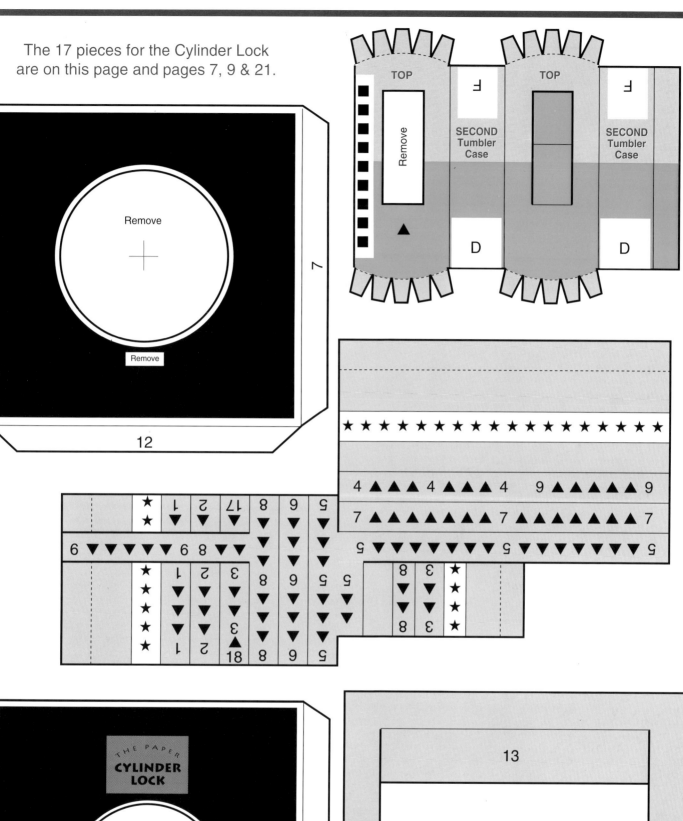

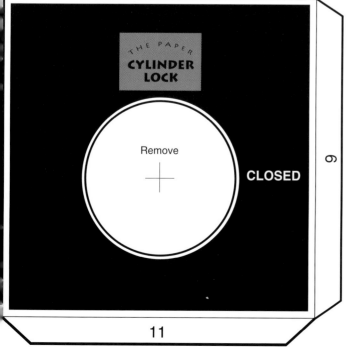

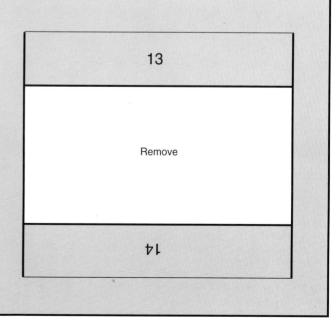

F F F F   F F F F F

▼

Second Tumbler Case
**CYLINDER
LOCK**

8   8

8   8

C C C C C   C C C C C

■■■■■■■■■■■■■■■■■   8

Key Support
**CYLINDER
LOCK**

Front
**CYLINDER
LOCK**

■■■■■■■■■■■■■■■

★★★★★★★★★★★★★★★★★★★★

12
12

10   10

10   10

11   12

Base
**CYLINDER
LOCK**

10

Back
**CYLINDER
LOCK**

12

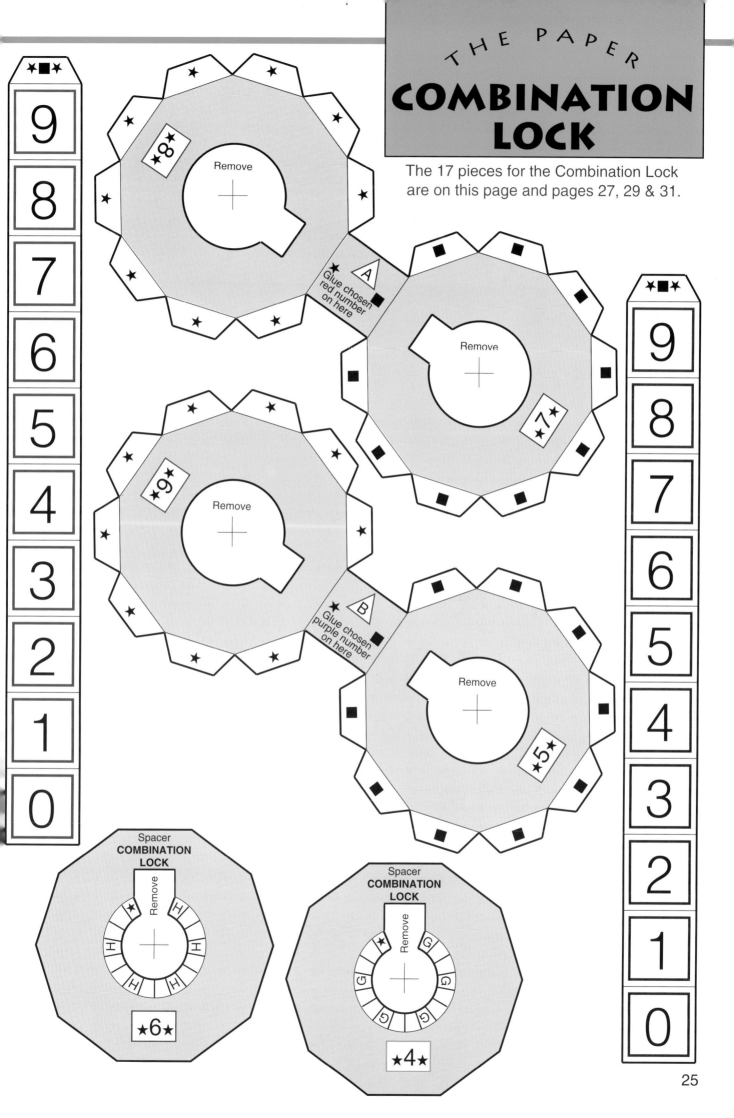

THE PAPER
COMBINATION LOCK

The 17 pieces for the Combination Lock are on this page and pages 27, 29 & 31.

★■★

9
8
7
6
5
4
3
2
1
0

★■★

9
8
7
6
5
4
3
2
1
0

★8★
Remove

★ A
Glue chosen red number on here

Remove
★7★

★9★
Remove

★ B
Glue chosen purple number on here

Remove
★5★

Spacer
COMBINATION LOCK
Remove
H H H H H H H
★6★

Spacer
COMBINATION LOCK
Remove
G G G G G G G
★4★

Number
Strip

COMBINATION
LOCK

Number Block
COMBINATION
LOCK

Number
Strip

COMBINATION
LOCK

Number Block
COMBINATION
LOCK

★■★

★5★

★7★

26

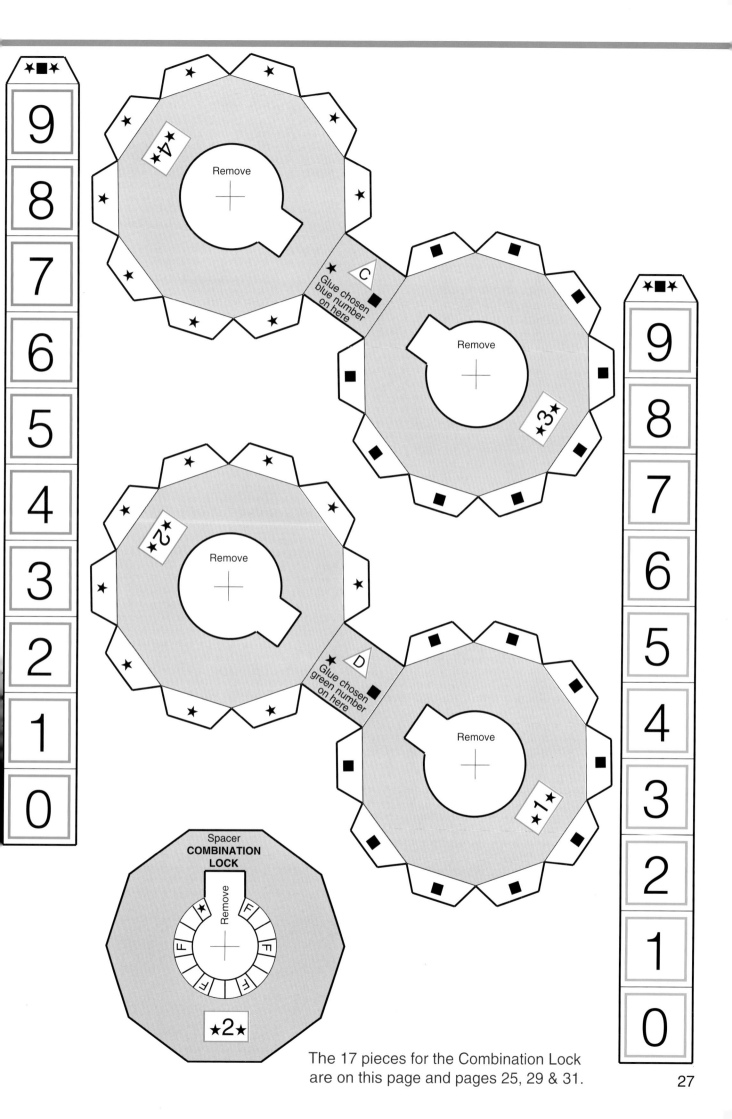

The 17 pieces for the Combination Lock
are on this page and pages 25, 29 & 31.

Number
Strip

D COMBINATION
LOCK

D

Number Block
COMBINATION
LOCK

C
Number
Strip

C COMBINATION
LOCK

C

C

Number Block
COMBINATION
LOCK

C

C

C

C

C

D

D

D

D

D

D

D

★■★

★3★

★■★

28

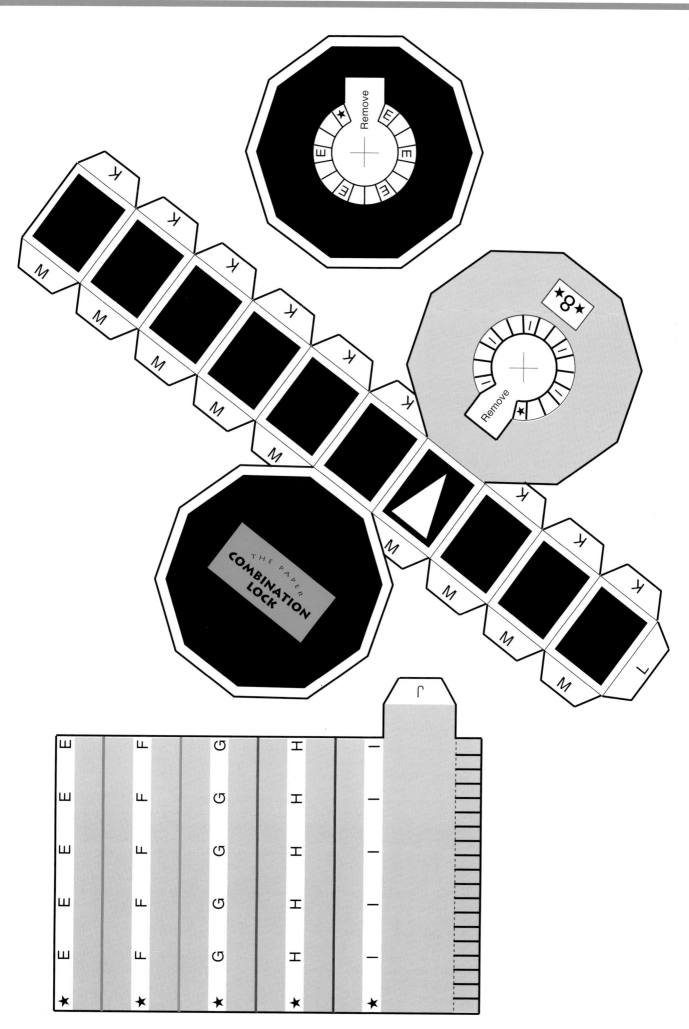

The 17 pieces for the Combination Lock are on this page and pages 25, 27 & 31.

★1★

End of
Number Barrel
**COMBINATION
LOCK**

Number Barrel
**COMBINATION
LOCK**

J

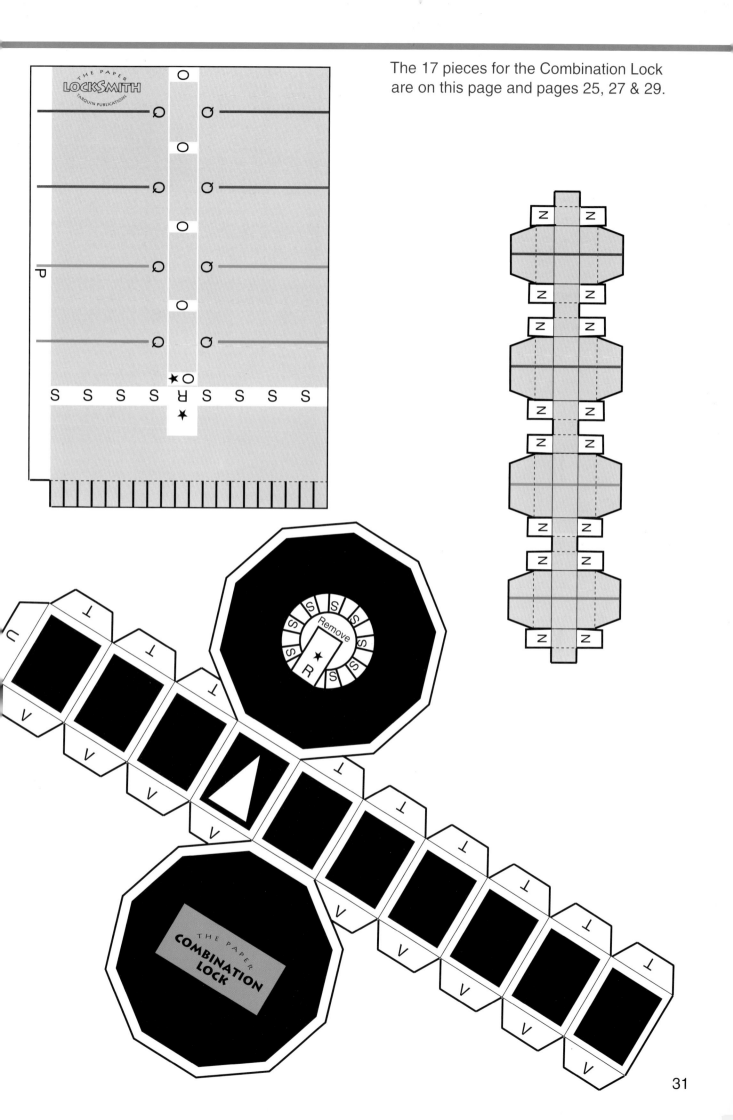

The 17 pieces for the Combination Lock are on this page and pages 25, 27 & 29.

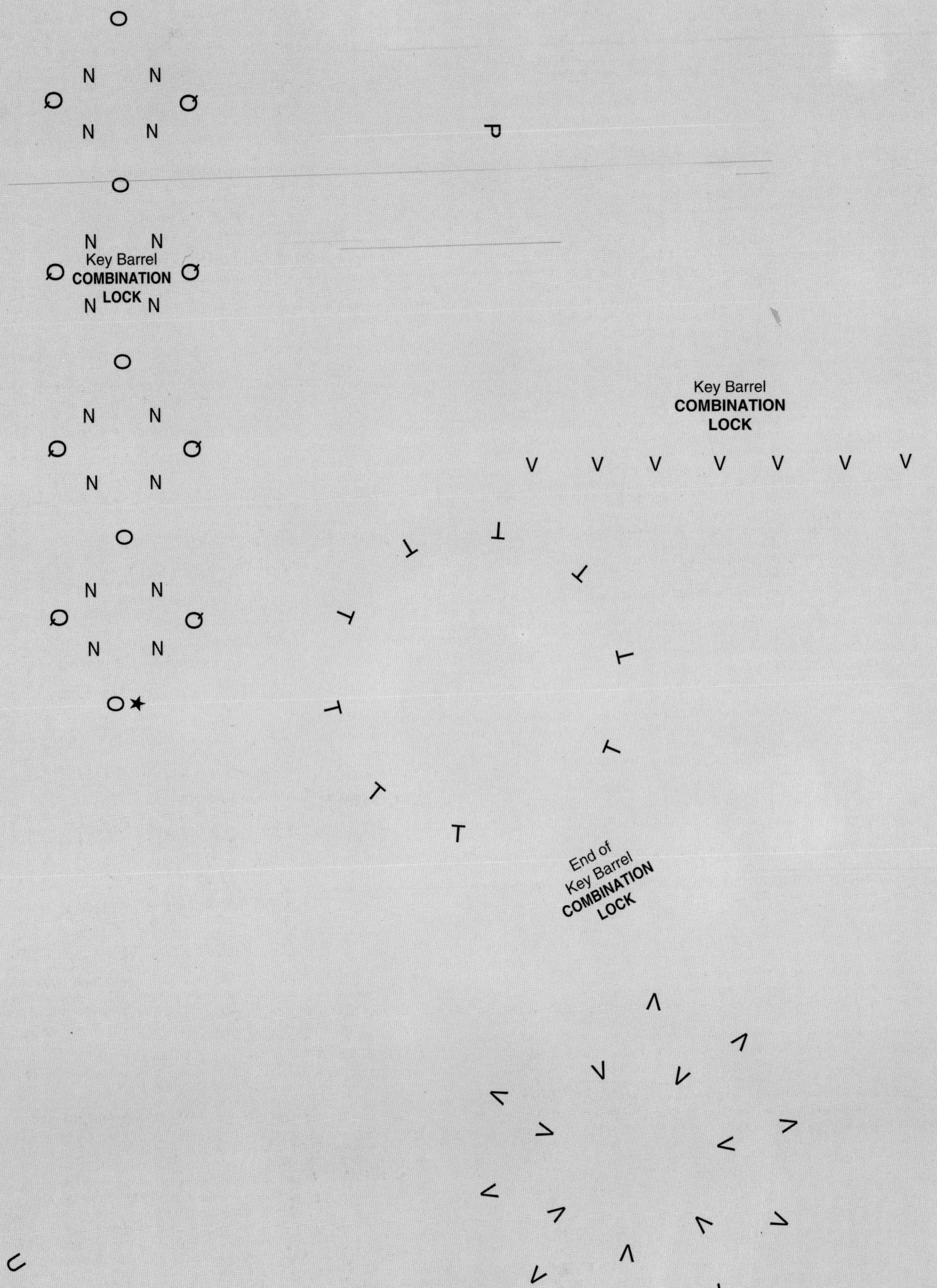

O

N N

O O

N N

P

O

N N

Key Barrel
COMBINATION
N **LOCK** N

O O

O

N N

O O

N N

Key Barrel
COMBINATION
LOCK

V V V V V V V

O

T

N N

T

O O

T

N N

T

O★

T

T

T

End of
Key Barrel
COMBINATION
LOCK